of Northumbria

For Helen, William and Kitty

The following stories are based on traditional folklore
and legends from the North East of England.

First published in the United Kingdom in 2007 by Northern Heritage Services Limited.

First published in the
United Kingdom in 2007 by
Northern Heritage Services Limited

Northern Heritage Services Limited
Unit 7
New Kennels
Blagdon Estate
Seaton Burn
Newcastle upon Tyne
NE13 6DB

Text copyright:
© 2007 Northern Heritage

Illustrations copyright:
© 2007 Gary Hogg

Design and layout:
Ian Scott Design

ISBN: 978-0-9544777-7-6

Printed and bound by
Compass Press Limited.

British Library Cataloguing in
Publishing Data: a catalogue record
for this book is available from the
British Library.

Contents

THE GREY MAN OF BELLISTER

Lord Blenkinsopp was a mean, unfriendly man. Suspicious and distrustful of others, the lord hated strangers most of all…

So if ever a needy traveller appeared at the gates of his home, Bellister Castle, near Haltwhistle, they would be turned away. Except on one windswept night.

On this particular night, an old travelling minstrel walked up to the castle gates. "Please take pity, sire, on a poor traveller in need of food and shelter," he begged.

As he didn't have a penny to his name, the traveller offered tales and songs as payment. To the surprise of the servants at the castle, the lord welcomed him in.

But the mean old man's generosity didn't last long. Soon, all manner of suspicious thoughts were racing through his brain.

"Who is this stranger I have welcomed into my home?" the lord asked himself. "I must have been out of my mind! Is he a thief, an outlaw, or even worse a murderer?"

Soon the minstrel announced that he was tired and was shown to his room. But the distrustful lord wasn't taking any chances.

"Wait a while, then check my guest's room to see if he's warm and comfortable," he ordered a servant. The lord was horrified by what the servant discovered: the stranger's bed was empty!

Of course, Lord Blenkinsopp didn't know the true reason why the minstrel was missing. As the evening had gone on, the man had become unsettled by his host's unfriendly manner and, feeling under threat, he had stepped outside into the night for some fresh air.

But the lord had already made up his mind. "This so-called minstrel is planning to slit my throat and steal my wealth," he thought to himself. "This is what I get for being such a generous host!"

So the lord ordered a servant to gather his hounds and he took out a search party to hunt for this "dangerous scoundrel".

With the lord and his servants close behind, the dogs soon scented their prey and the traveller had no choice but to run.

"Saints protect me!" cried the man as he was chased all the way to the banks of the river Tyne. "I am but an old man, but if I stop, I am a dead man too."

However, exhaustion eventually took hold of the poor minstrel and, with no more energy left, he collapsed to his knees.

"A-ha! Now I have you!" cried the lord. But before he could order them off, the hungry dogs seized their chance and tore their prey limb from limb.

Once word of the minstrel's grisly death had spread, Lord Blenkinsopp was not bothered by any more visits from hungry, weary travellers. Except one.

This haunting visitor, whose grey face was disfigured by an ugly, bloody gash, was more unwelcome than any the lord had ever encountered – or could ever have imagined.

This terrifying figure would not ask for food or shelter. In fact, he would not say a single word. Instead, he just gave a chilling stare and pointed an accusing finger at the man who had brought about his death.

And to this day, locals say that, on a calm night, you can still hear the hounds pursuing their prey, and the bloodcurdling screams of the Grey Man of Bellister.

Every week of the year, castles and manor houses across Northumberland play host to lavish, romantic weddings. But Featherstone Castle and its woods have become known for some very unusual – and ghostly – nuptials.

Our story takes place many years ago, on the wedding day of Abigail Featherstonehaugh, the daughter of the castle's owner at the time, Baron Featherstonehaugh.

It wasn't to be a happy day for Abigail. The baron had made all the arrangements: his daughter was to marry a distant relative, Timothy Featherstonehaugh, but it was not he who Abigail loved. Her heart belonged to another man, Ridley of Hardriding, but their romance was doomed because of a longstanding feud between the two families.

When he had found out about his daughter's feelings for Ridley, the baron – a stubborn and unreasonable man – ordered that she never see her lover again, and immediately set out to find a more 'suitable' husband for Abigail.

So the baron's plans went ahead, and a distraught Abigail was married to Timothy in the castle chapel.

To follow the lavish ceremony, a banquet in honour of the new bride and groom had been arranged. But before it could begin, tradition demanded that

the entire wedding party go out for a ride in the castle grounds.

"Farewell," bid the baron as the group set off. "I pray your ride gives you an appetite, for a sumptuous feast will greet you on your return."

The baron watched as the wedding party rode off, then put his servants to work, setting out the tables. When everything was in place, they waited for the riders to return. And waited.

However, hours later, there was still no sign of them. Anxious about their whereabouts, the baron sent out a few of his most trusted men to look for the missing group, but their search was fruitless.

"We traced their route not once but twice, sire," explained the leader of the search party. "But they could not be found. It is as if they have disappeared into thin air."

As midnight approached, the baron's anxiety turned to despair. But then, just as the witching hour arrived, the clatter of horses' hooves was heard on the castle drawbridge.

Suddenly, the front door burst open and, accompanied by a blast of icy cold air, the missing wedding guests entered the Great Hall.

"Oh, thank the Lord!" exclaimed the baron. "I had feared the worst! Come, be seated and let the festivities begin. But pray tell me, what kept…"

But the baron didn't finish his sentence, for as he watched the guests walk to their seats, not a single breath or footstep could be heard. And as an unearthly silence filled the hall, he could not believe what he was witnessing – some of the guests passed through tables as if they weren't there!

Frozen to the spot, the baron stared at the white, expressionless faces of the bride, groom and the rest of the group. Suddenly, the horrible truth became clear: this was not a wedding celebration, this was a party of ghosts!

Baron Featherstonehaugh screamed with terror and fainted to the ground. When he was eventually awoken by a servant, the spectral assembly had vanished.

Little had he known what had befallen the wedding party after they had left the castle: they had been the victims of an ambush that went horribly wrong.

A gang led by Abigail's lover, Ridley of Hardriding, had jumped out at the riders as they headed back towards the castle. His plan was to save his beloved from the fate of an unhappy marriage and whisk her off so they could start a new life together.

But the ambush became more bloody and violent than Ridley had foreseen, and all those involved were killed – including the ill-fated lovers.

Legend has it that Ridley was so grief-stricken by Abigail's death, he plunged a dagger into his own heart and his blood flowed into a nearby hollow stone and was drunk by ravens. From that day, this stone has been known as the "Raven's Stone".

There was another victim of the ambush who hadn't been present: the baron himself. The father of the bride was so shaken and upset by the incident, he became paralysed and never spoke another word until the day he died.

It is said that, even now, the blood-chilling sound of clattering hooves can be heard in the woods near Featherstone Castle every year on the anniversary of that terrible day. The wedding party has returned once more.

GREEN JANE OF BAMBURGH

In the shadow of the majestic Bamburgh Castle on the Northumbrian coast...

there once lived a young girl named Jane. Life was hard for Jane and her family, who were so poor they often went without food.

One day, fearing that they would starve to death, Jane's father took her to one side.

"Oh, my precious daughter," he complained miserably. "You know what a proud man your father is, and how I have always tried my best to provide for this family. But now I must swallow my pride and ask for the help of others, or else none of us will survive much longer."

So, reluctantly, he sent her to the castle to appeal to its wealthy owners and beg for any scraps of food they could spare.

Draped in a threadbare green cloak, Jane set off to the castle on her mission of mercy. In her arms, she carried her baby sister. Her father had hoped that the plight of the pale, sickly child would soften the hearts of those at the castle.

"Do not cry, my love," she whispered to the baby. "No noble heart could cast an eye on such a pretty face as yours and turn us away from his door."

Despite these words of comfort, Jane trembled with fear as she climbed the steep stairs to the castle's postern gate. She became even more terrified when she spied the guards eyeing her as she approached.

"P-p-please, kind sirs… please have mercy on a poor local girl whose family are without food and will surely starve without the help of the kind lord and lady of the castle…"

Little had she reckoned on the heartlessness of the guards, however. Before she could say another word, the wicked pair burst into cruel, mocking laughter.

"Do you really think our master would have pity on the likes of you?" sneered one of

the men, looking Jane up and down with disgust. "Get home to your people this minute, lest your pathetic whining puts everyone off their food."

Jane was so stunned she couldn't speak. Dizzy from hunger and with the guards' mocking laughter ringing in her ears, the poor girl stumbled as she turned away to descend the stairs and she lost her footing.

With an piercing cry, Jane plummeted to the ground. Tragically, both Jane and the baby sister she was still clutching in her arms died in the fall.

So, if you ever pay a visit to Bamburgh Castle, keep an eye – and an ear – out for 'Green Jane'.

Some claim to have seen Jane dressed in the distinctive green cloak that provides her nickname, tumbling down the steep stairway from the postern gate with a small bundle in her arms. But when they have rushed to her aid, no victim could be found.

Witnesses also report the sound of wicked-sounding male laughter, followed by a girl's cry so distressing it's not easily forgotten.

THE CAULD LAD O' HYLTON

Way back in the
16th century,
there lived
a young lad named
Robert Skelton…

Robert was employed as a stable lad at Hylton Castle in Sunderland, and among his jobs was preparing the mount of the castle's owner, Robert Hylton.

The 12-year-old boy enjoyed his job, but it was demanding, tiring work and each night he would sleep soundly in his bed till sunrise.

One day, young Robert was labouring away in the stables when tiredness got the better of him and he had to take a break.

"My master's horse must be saddled," he said to himself as he lay back on a bed of hay. "He will be angry if his mount is not ready. But all my energy is gone and my eyelids feel as heavy as two lumps of lead." With that, he drifted off to sleep.

But little did Robert realise how angry the baron would be. The boy awoke with a start to find his master standing over him, his face red with rage.

"What is this? Asleep when you should be hard at work?" boomed the baron. "I'll have you whipped, you idle boy. Where is my mount?"

Robert was so terrified he couldn't answer and he struggled to get up. But the stable lad he never made it to his feet.

When his master saw that his horse was not ready, this made him madder still. Quivering with anger, the baron grabbed a nearby pitchfork and swung it at Robert, removing his head from his body.

Quick to disguise his murderous deed, the baron disposed of his victim's dismembered body in a deep pond in the shadow of the castle.

From that day, it is said, the shivering spirit of poor Robert Skelton wandered the grounds of the castle, looking for a warm place to rest.

The servants in the castle kitchen were the first to become aware of his presence.

Robert's naked ghost – sometimes carrying his head under his arm – was often seen in that area of the castle, leaving a trail of blood where he had walked.

He would also play pranks, such as torturing the castle's cats by tying their tails together and moving objects in the kitchen.

His favourite trick was throwing around dishes and plates – but only if the kitchen had been left in a tidy state. If it were ever left in a messy state, the cheeky lad would tidy it up! The servants soon got wise to this and began to leave the kitchen untidy at night.

Hot ashes would be taken from the fire and found by the kitchen staff in the morning with the imprint of a small boy's body in them, and chamber pots would be emptied onto the floor.

The mischievous antics of the 'Cauld Lad' – as the servants came to call the ghost because of his unclothed, shivering appearance – were not confined to the castle itself.

It is said the spectre also took great delight in impersonating the boatman of the nearby Hylton ferry and, after taking his passengers' fares, would leave the unsuspecting folk stranded in the middle of the river!

And the Cauld Lad was often seen in the kitchen after midnight, sitting forlornly on the edge of the table with his legs dangling, singing of his fate.

"Wae's me, wae's me," he would sing.
"The acorn's not yet fallen from the tree.
That's to grow the wood,

That's to make the cradle,
That's to rock the bairn,
That's to grow to the man
That's to lay me!"

One night, one of the castle maids was passing the kitchen when she suddenly heard the Cauld Lad's song. She crept to the doorway and spied the ghost perched on a table, lamenting how cold he was.

Touched by his plight, the kindly maid took pity on the wretched soul and resolved to help him.

"Oh, it broke my heart to see the poor little dear shivering like that," said the maid to her husband as she described what she had seen. "But I know just the thing to bring a smile to his little face."

So she took up her needle and thread and sewed the Cauld Lad a fine green cloak and hood to keep out the chill. The next day, when she had finished her chores at the castle, the maid left the present in front of the kitchen fire.

That night, she and her husband hid behind a door and waited for the Cauld Lad to appear. Sure enough, around midnight, the young ghost materialized before their eyes.

As the couple watched, they saw the lad's eyes drawn to the hood and cloak, and he let out a yelp of joy. Grinning from ear to ear, he tried it on – and it fitted perfectly.

Then, as quickly as he had appeared, the Cauld Lad vanished with this verse: "Here's a cloak and here's a hood, The Cauld Lad o' Hylton will do no more good."

And this tragic little ghost hasn't been seen or heard at Hylton Castle since that day.

THE MURDEROUS LOVERS OF KNARESDALE

Four miles from Haltwhistle sits Knaresdale Hall…

Legend has it that, many years ago, the ancient mansion was owned by a middle-aged laird whose wealth won him the hand of a beautiful young woman.

Despite her own strong reservations about the arrangement, in the end she bowed to pressure from her parents and married the laird, and for a time it appeared that the young woman had settled into her new life.

But her marriage wasn't the reason for her apparent happiness. Unbeknownst to the laird, his wife had fallen in love with his nephew, a handsome young man living at Knaresdale Hall along with his sister.

The lovers would meet in secret, never once arousing the suspicions of the laird. "But we must take care," the young man would tell his beloved. "My uncle does not know what is going on under his roof, but if he did, neither of our lives would be worth living."

"Oh, do not worry about him," the laird's wife would reply. "He's nothing but an ignorant old fool. He'll never find out."

But then, one day, they were spotted in an embrace by the laird's niece. She loved her brother and vowed to herself that their secret would stay just that, but the laird's young wife was frightened that the girl would tell all to their benefactor.

"No, she will cause us no trouble," the young man reassured her. "My sister's love for me is so deep, she would never do or say anything that would cause me harm."

Yet although he pleaded with her, the laird's nephew couldn't convince his lover that his sister would remain quiet – she had already resolved to silence the girl for good. And so besotted was the young man that he agreed to her murderous plan.

So, one night, as the wind and rain raged outside, howling and rattling windows, the laird's wife woke suddenly and turned to her husband.

"Can you hear that?" she complained. "The door of one of the outbuildings is banging in the storm and keeping me from my sleep. Be a caring husband and shut it for me."

She knew the laird was a lazy and thoughtless man, and once he had retired to bed he was reluctant to leave it. So, as she had expected, he called his niece and ordered her to carry out the thankless task.

As she ventured outside to locate the noisy door, little did the poor girl suspect her brother was lurking in the shadows with murderous intent.

Blinded by his love for his uncle's beautiful wife, he grabbed his sister and pulled her outside into the storm. Then he dragged her to a nearby lake and pushed her in.

As she fought for her life, he held her under the water, and when she had gasped her final breath, the young man floated his sister's body into the middle of the lake and watched it sink without trace.

With the storm still battering the house, the laird began to felt a tinge of guilt at having sent his niece out on such a treacherous night.

"The rain is as fierce as ever," he said to his wife. "And the wind shows no sign of abating, either. Perhaps I should ensure she has returned safely to her bed."

"Rest easy and do not worry," she replied. "I will do it."

Of course, the devious young woman knew that by now her husband's niece would be

dead, so instead of checking the girl's bedroom, she merely waited for a few minutes in a corridor close by, before returning.

"Go back to sleep and do not worry more," she reported. "Your niece is safe and well."

But then, in the early hours, the laird was woken by the sound of his dogs howling.

Sitting up in bed, he looked over towards the fireplace in his bedroom and he saw his niece standing there, wringing out her wet clothes. He was just about to apologise for sending her out into the unrelenting storm when, to his astonishment, she disappeared.

The girl wasn't the only person to vanish that night – his nephew, who committed the deadly act, was also never seen again.

That fateful night also took its toll on the laird's wife. Consumed by guilt about her crime and distraught about the disappearance of her lover, she collapsed into a fever the next day and eventually admitted to the plot.

Sure enough, when the pond was trawled, the body of the laird's tragic niece was found. By this time, his wife had gone insane and, soon after, she died.

But there has been no rest for the victim of her crime. It is said the drenched, howling form of the laird's niece visits the hall each year on the anniversary of her death, and has been seen walking near the lake.

And the door of one of the outbuildings is said to bang open and closed of its own accord, just as it did that fateful, stormy night.

THE MAID OF MELDON

A resident of Meldon, just a few miles west of Morpeth, Margaret Selby was an unattractive and thoroughly mean-spirited woman.

The daughter of a Newcastle money lender, she had inherited his miserly nature, so there was surprise among some of her neighbours when word spread that she had found herself a husband.

We say *some* of her neighbours because not all were surprised by this development; after all, Margaret had a sizeable dowry, which included the mortgage on Meldon Hall. The man she was set to marry was a widower named Sir William Fenwick of Wallington, and he was well aware of Margaret's favourable financial situation.

But if Sir William had indeed planned to get his hands on his wife's money, he never got the chance, for he died before her.

Following his death, an effigy of Sir William was put in the Church of St John The Baptist in Meldon and it wasn't long before his widow returned to the true love of her life: expanding her fortune. Margaret decided to take complete charge of the properties and estates of Meldon Hall herself, and she threw herself into the task, proving to be a very accomplished farmer.

This new arrangement generated money – plenty of it. And, being miserly by nature, as we have said, Margaret guarded her growing wealth with her life.

"I must take great caution," she would mutter to herself as she counted her money. "For there are some who would swipe my money from under my nose as swiftly as my back was turned."

So, each day, as she became more obsessive about protecting her hoard, Margaret would find new and yet more undetectable places to hide it, and she became increasingly secretive with her movements.

It is even claimed that this greedy individual built a tunnel between Meldon Hall and her other residence, Hartington Hall, near Rothley, so that she and her money could pass between the two estates undetected.

But, of course, there was one thing Margaret's money could not protect her against, and when the day of her death finally came, she was buried at Newminster Abbey.

But the story does not end there. It is said the miserly Margaret was so distraught at being parted with her beloved fortune that, even after her death, she can still be seen looking for her hidden hoard.

Some locals claim to have seen her ghost sitting on a stone trough in the graveyard of Newminster Abbey; others say she rushes back and forth across the bridge in Meldon that crosses the river Wansbeck, desperately searching for the sites where she hid her considerable wealth.

Even stranger are the reports that the Maid Of Meldon, as she has become known, has been sighted in the shape of a black dog, which, to the astonishment of onlookers, transforms into a beautiful woman before their very eyes.

Whichever form she takes, the story goes that her spirit roams the area for seven years, then rests for another seven before resuming its search. Perhaps one day she will locate her cherished trove and finally find rest…

THE FLOWER OF BEDLINGTON

In the village of Bedlington in Northumberland, there once lived a young girl...

who was so beautiful in appearance and lovely by nature, she was known by all who had made her acquaintance as "The Flower of Bedlington".

She had many admirers, but there was only one man in her heart: a young, poor ploughman named James Robson.

Despite being a fine young man, well-liked for his manners and his hard-working attitude, he could gain no favour with his loved one's parents. Wealthy but mean-minded, they did not see James as a match for their daughter, whom they intended to marry off to a rich man at the first possible opportunity.

So they tried every trick they could to split up the lovers. But their attempts were unsuccessful, and when the bond between the young pair remained as strong as ever, the parents took extreme measures, sending their daughter to Stokesley in North Yorkshire to live at her uncle's farm.

The "Flower" and her beau were distraught at the news, and when the day came to bid goodbye, she made a pledge:

"Of love and truth through life sincere
Nor death should part
For from the grave
Short time should the survivor save."

But their parting was all too much for James; less than a week after the split, he died of a broken heart. His lover's wicked parents were thrilled by this news: James had been the only obstacle to their plans to marry off their daughter to someone more "befitting her status and wealth", and now that obstacle was gone. And they had already lined up a very suitable young gentleman…

On the very day that James' funeral took place nearby, the selfish couple made

arrangements for their daughter's wedding: they would bring their daughter home to Bedlington the next day and she would be married without delay. Satisfied with their plans, the pair retired to bed early.

At the stroke of midnight that night, there was a visitor at the uncle's farm in Stokesley. It was James. He had come to collect his loved one on her father's finest steeds. Rapping on the front door, he called out: "I am here for you, my love, so be quick. I have brought your mother's best cloak and hood to keep you warm, for we have a long ride back to your parents' house."

The girl was surprised by James' unannounced arrival, and when her uncle joined her at the door, he was suspicious. But then he spied the clothes that the young man had spoken of, and also the horse.

"Your father would never have allowed his grey mare to be ridden without his consent," her uncle said. "So I know everything this young man says is true. You may leave with my blessing. And God speed you on your journey, for it is a perishingly cold night."

It was also very dark, with the moon hidden by the clouds for most of their journey. At one point as they rode along, James commented that he had a pain in his head. Keen to ease his suffering, the girl put her hand to his brow.

"Heavens above!" she exclaimed. "You are as cold as ice, my love. Here, let me wrap my scarf around your neck."

But she got an even bigger surprise when the moon reappeared from behind the clouds. As she looked towards the ground, the girl noticed something very strange: both her and the horse's shadows could clearly be seen, but there was no sign of James'!

Before she had time to question this, they arrived at her parents' house, and James helped her down from the horse.

"Go inside and warm your bones, and I'll take your father's horse to the stable and feed her. She's carried us a long distance tonight and she needs rest as badly as we do."

When her parents answered the door, they were astonished by her arrival. But their daughter was too overcome with emotion to let them speak.

"Oh, Mother, Father…" she gushed. "Thank you for accepting my love for James. When you sent him to bring me back home, I could hardly believe it…"

Neither could her parents. As she continued with the details of her journey, the girl's father went as white as a sheet and began to tremble uncontrollably. He could not believe it was true – had not her suitor been buried that very day?

Sick with fright, he plucked up the courage to go to the stable. To his relief, there was no sign of James… but his finest mare was drenched with sweat and clearly exhausted. His daughter's story had been true!

Meanwhile, the girl's mother broke the terrible news of her lover's death. It was all too much for the girl to take. At first, she fell mute with shock, then she screamed and collapsed in a faint. Pale and shaking, she was carried to her bed.

Over the next few weeks, the girl was examined by many doctors, but none could find a reason for her state. All they could say for sure was that her days were numbered.

Before she died, there was just one moment that she was able to speak: her final request was that she be buried in the same coffin as her loved one. Her grief-stricken parents agreed without hestitation.

But there is one final twist in this tale. When the day of her funeral came, James' coffin was opened and her parents were stunned by what they saw. There, draped around the dead man's neck, was their daughter's scarf.

THE WHITE LADY OF CRESSWELL

In the small hamlet of Cresswell, near Newbiggin-By-The-Sea, there once lived a baron, his daughter and his three sons…

The baron's beautiful daughter had fallen in love with a Danish prince who owned a small fort just a few miles away, and the pair made plans to marry.

"Oh, my love," the prince would say to his beloved. "I cannot wait for the day when we will be husband and wife. But there is one thing that stands in the way of our future happiness."

That one thing was, in fact, three: the girl's brothers. They hated the prince and would do anything they could to stop their sister marrying a Dane.

"For the sake of our family's name, we cannot allow our sister to marry that… that foreigner!" one of the brothers cried in disgust. "No, we must prevent it at all costs."

So the trio hatched a deadly plan. The next time the prince came to visit, they would lie in wait in the sand dunes along the route, then jump out and kill him.

That day came and, as expected, the prince took his usual route, singing happily to himself as he rode to see his loved one. But when he passed the brothers' hiding place, they saw their chance – and seized it.

"Brothers, let us do our duty!" bellowed the first of the brothers to pounce. Spears

and swords in hand, the murderous trio attacked the Danish prince, knocking their unsuspecting victim from his horse.

But as he fell, the prince's foot became caught in his stirrup, and as his frightened, injured horse galloped onwards towards his lover's home, Cresswell Tower, the dying man was dragged along the ground.

The baron's daughter had been excited about the prospect of seeing her love, and had climbed the steps to the top of the tower to watch his arrival. But as she looked out, she could only watch helplessly as she saw her brothers carry out their evil deed.

"My love, what have they done to you?!" she cried, wringing her hands in torment. "My eyes must be deceiving me. This cannot be true!"

But then the full horror of what she had witnessed sank in, and her fright turned into an insane frenzy and hatred of her three brothers. "I curse you!" she hollered from the tower. "I curse you all, murderers of my beloved prince, to meet your end before a year has passed!"

Looking down, the baron's daughter

saw the prince's horse arrive at the tower and collapse to the ground, panting its final breath. Still hanging from the stirrup was the prince, who had died from his wounds.

It was all too much for the baron's daughter to take. Not wanting to live without her loved one, she threw herself from the tower. She broke her neck in the fall and died, landing beside her beloved prince.

But her curse lived on. Within a year, as she had vowed, all three brothers had perished. The first was killed during a battle with the Scots. The second met his end when he was thrown from his horse while out hunting one day; like the Danish prince, he became caught in the stirrups and was dragged along the ground. As for the third brother, he was drowned when his boat capsized.

The baron's daughter had had her revenge, but the story doesn't end there.

Ever since that dreadful day, on the anniversary of the tragic lovers' death, a lady dressed in white is seen looking out from the top of Cresswell Tower. Witnesses say she seems to be watching and waiting for someone's arrival.

Then the clattering of a horse's hooves is heard and, with an agonizing wail, the White Lady of Cresswell disappears for another year.

THE GHOSTS OF CHILLINGHAM CASTLE

Chillingham Castle is famed for several reasons…

One of these is its herd of cattle, a unique and distinctive white-coated breed that has roamed wild in its grounds for over 700 years. But this majestic castle near Alnwick is perhaps better known for a more disturbing feature – it is reputed to be one of the most haunted places in Britain. Here are the stories of two of its most illustrious and most often sighted ghosts…

In the late 16th century, England was at war with Spain and, as often happens during conflict between countries, each side deployed spies to try to uncover the other's battle plans. These spies were well trained in avoiding detection, and would do anything to prevent their activities being revealed – even commit cold-blooded murder.

The story goes that, one day, a boy working at Chillingham Castle made a discovery that would prove to be his undoing.

The lad was going about his duties as usual, when he overheard two men having a conversation in a room nearby. He would not normally have listened in to what they were saying – he was far too honest – but their discussion intrigued him. One of the men seemed to briefing the other about a fleet of enemy ships heading for the English Channel – a Spanish Armada!

Their conversation over, the two men left the room and walked away, but the boy's curiosity got the better of him and he went to investigate. Entering the room, he saw some papers on a table and, after checking that he was alone, he walked over and began to read them.

The lad quickly realised how much danger his country was in, but just as he had thrust some of the sheets into his shirt, he heard a sound at the doorway. One of the men had returned and caught him red-handed!

"A-ha!" said the man with a menacing look on his face. "What have we here? You have made a very grave mistake, my boy…"

With that, the spy grabbed him by the arms and bundled him down the hall to where the other man was waiting. "It seems our young friend here has taken quite an interest in our plans," he said to his associate. "But we can't have him letting anyone else know about them, can we?"

The men had a truly evil solution: they took the poor unfortunate boy to an unoccupied room in the castle and walled him up alive. Despite his calls for help, no one heard his desperate cries and, days later, he died in his claustrophobic cell.

But even in death, the lad refused to be ignored. Many years later, overnight guests staying in one room at the castle – the Pink Room – reported hearing a terrible wailing at midnight and seeing a strange blue light glowing close to the old four-poster bed.

There was more: some visitors claimed to have witnessed a young boy dressed in blue materialise from the wall and walk towards them. His clothing was said to be old-fashioned, but he did not frighten the guests – instead they described him as a friendly presence. The legend of the "Blue Boy", or "Radiant Boy", was born.

Then, in the 1920s, workmen at the castle made a gruesome discovery. After removing bricks from a wall in the Pink Room, they found the skeleton of the young boy, with shreds of his blue clothing still intact – along with decaying scraps of those traitorous documents. Closer examination of scratch marks on the wall, and also the worn-down bones of the poor lad's fingers, revealed his attempts at escape.

After the remains were given a proper burial, the Blue Boy was never seen again – at least not in human form. Guests still describe seeing strange blue flashes of light in the middle of the night, close to the wall in the Pink Room. Some have blamed an electrical fault, but, as others have pointed out, there are no electrics in the wall in question.

Could it be that the Radiant Boy is still not at peace?

Chillingham Castle's other famous ghostly resident is Lady Mary Berkeley, better known as the Grey Lady.

In the mid-17th century, Lady Mary lived at the castle with her husband, Ford Grey – Earl Of Tankerville and Lord of Wark and Chillingham – having inherited the Chillingham estate from the earl's father, Sir William Grey.

In 1678, Lady Mary was overjoyed at the birth of their baby daughter, also named Mary. But her happiness was to be short-lived…

Lady Mary had an 18-year-old sister named Henrietta, who lived at her father's house in Surrey in the south of England. Unbeknownst to his wife, Earl Grey had amorous intentions towards the young woman and, under the pretence of showing friendliness towards his sister-in-law, set about winning her heart.

Eventually, his plan worked and, despite her love for her sister Mary, the earl ensnared the impressionable Henrietta with his affections. But he had other intentions, too: as his wife looked after their daughter, the earl plotted with five of his associates to take Henrietta away from the family house undetected and start a new life with her.

So, one night, the earl and his cohorts travelled to Surrey and carried out their despicable plan, leaving Lady Mary alone in the castle, with only their baby daughter for company.

However, when the scandal broke, the earl and his associates where tracked down and brought to trial, charged with "unlawful tempting and inticing (of Lady Henrietta) to unlawful love, and carrying her away from her father's house... with an intent to cause her to live in a scandalous manner..." All but one was found guilty.

And what of Lady Mary? Well, the heartbroken woman never saw her husband again. But that's more than can be said for the lady herself. Many years after her death, visitors to Chillingham Castle have told of hearing the rustling of a dress in certain corridors, accompanied by a sudden icy chill in the air.

This isn't the only ghostly encounter reported: subsequent owners of Chillingham have described the frightening sight of Lady Mary's spectre "stepping out" of her portrait in the castle's Grey Room and following them around the castle.

Is the poor, deserted lady still searching for her wayward husband?